MC LONGNECK'S
EPIC
SPACE
ADVENTURE

ANDREW RADER
ILLUSTRATION BY GALEN FRAZER

StoryBook Genius
Publishing

www.sbgpublishing.com

A
ttention on
the pad...
we're sealing up the
ship! Strap in and start
the countdown — we're
ready for a trip!

B last off!
The engines roar
their mighty sound.

Hold on tight...
the rocket rises
off the ground.

C ruising through the clouds, we are leaving Earth behind. Up there out in space, who knows what things we'll find?

Docking at the station, we're here to resupply. There is a ton of awesome science at the lab up in the sky.

Enter lunar orbit,
and touchdown on the Moon.

Gravity is low so we can jump up to that dune.

F

lags, ships, and rovers lying all around. Footprints in the dust, covering lunar ground.

Get back inside our ship, our journey has begun!

150,000,000 KM

We fly across the solar system, heading for the Sun.

Heat and light are shining, intensely on our ship. We orbit at a distance, continuing our trip.

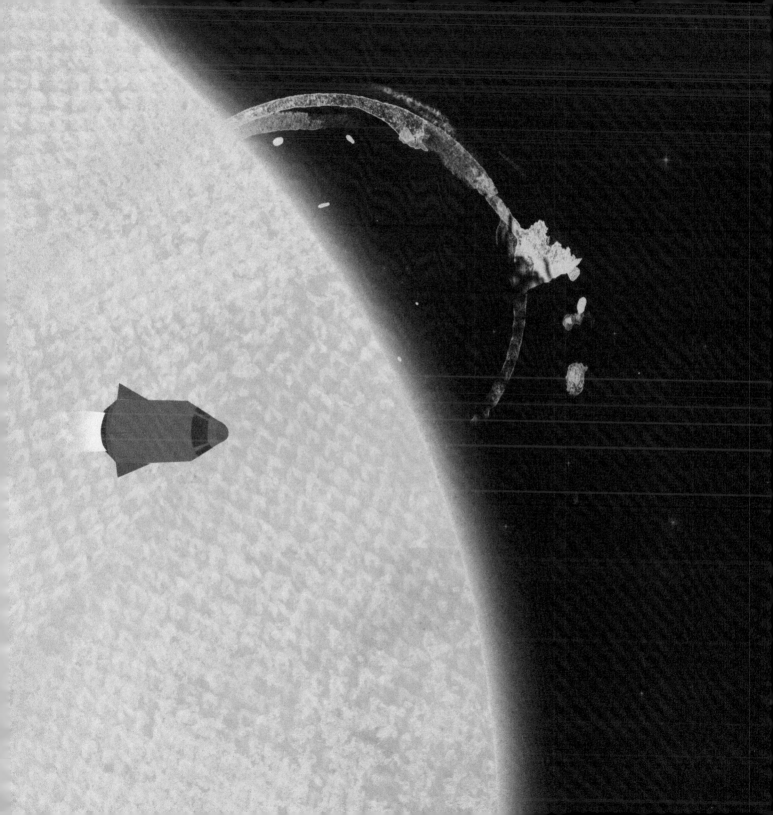

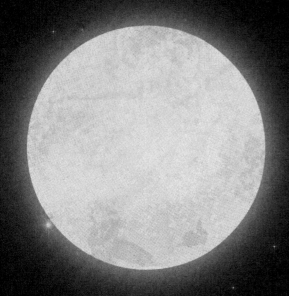

I nvestigating Mercury, we take a closer look.

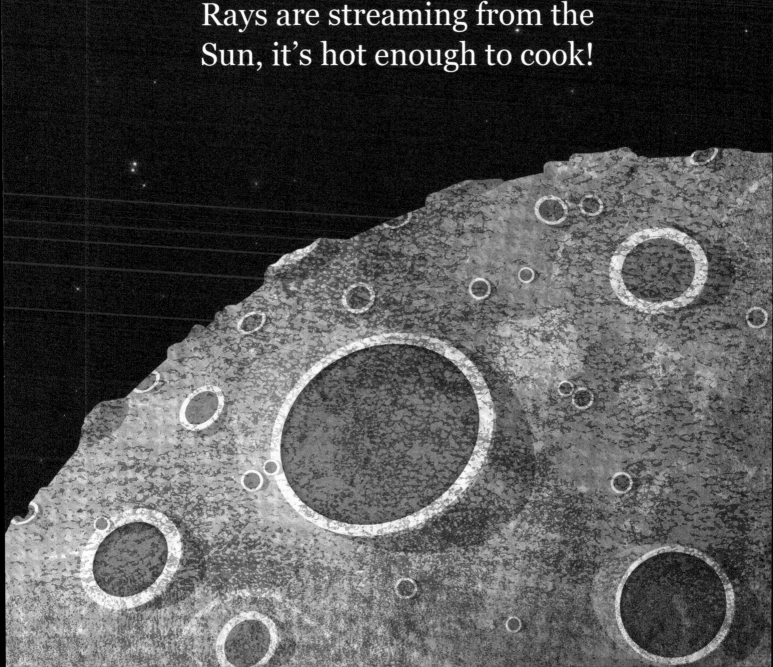

Rays are streaming from the
Sun, it's hot enough to cook!

J umping on to Venus, the hottest
planet yet. The rain is made of acid,
be careful — don't get wet!

K eeping the ship sealed tight,
through the clouds we fly.

Next we're on to Mars,
the red dot in the sky.

Landing is a challenge, the air is very thin. With parachute and thrusters, we touchdown on our fin.

M

ars is like a desert, but one that's really cold. A whole new world before us, what secrets does it hold?

Now climb the highest mountain, and explore the valley floor.

Let's relight our rocket,
and hear its mighty roar!

One and two in orbit, we count the moons of Mars. They're dwarfed against the planet, small rocks among the stars.

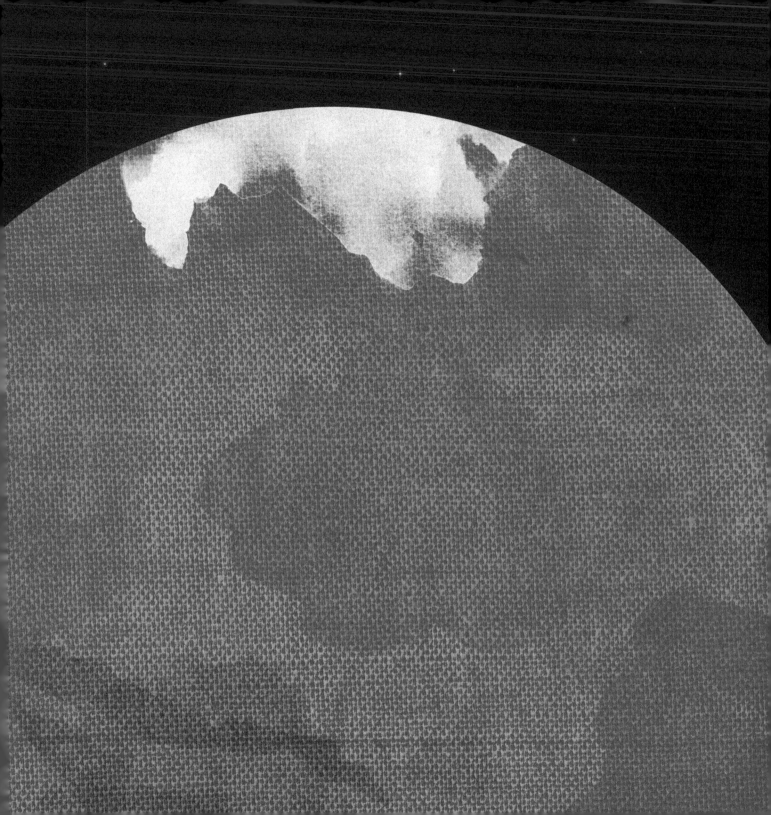

Past asteroids and comets, small worlds of ice and rock. With gravity so slight, you fly instead of walk.

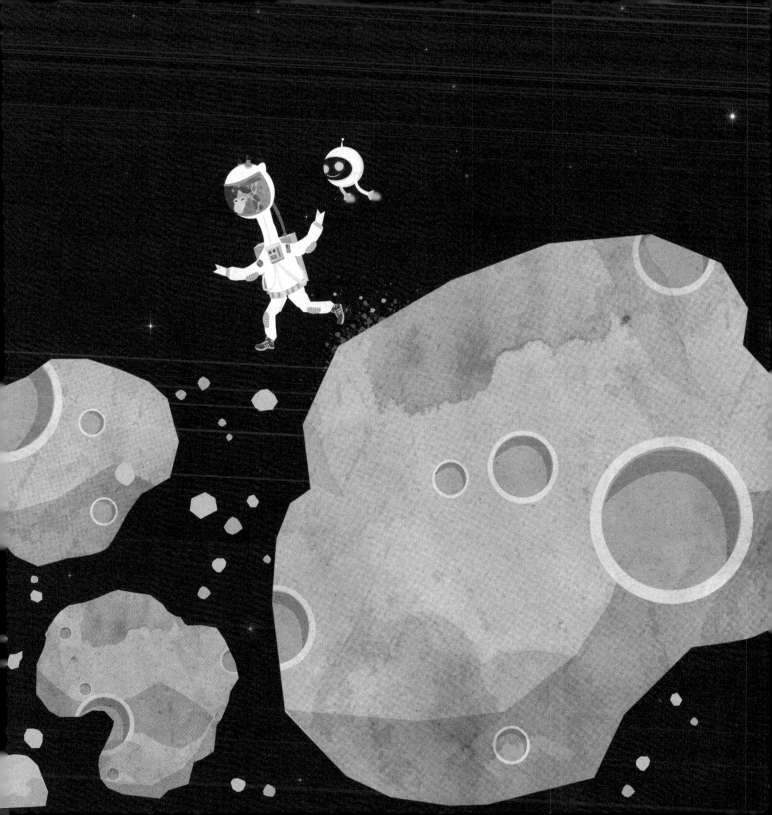

Quick! Back into the spaceship,
to Jupiter we go! The largest planet out
there, with four big moons to show.

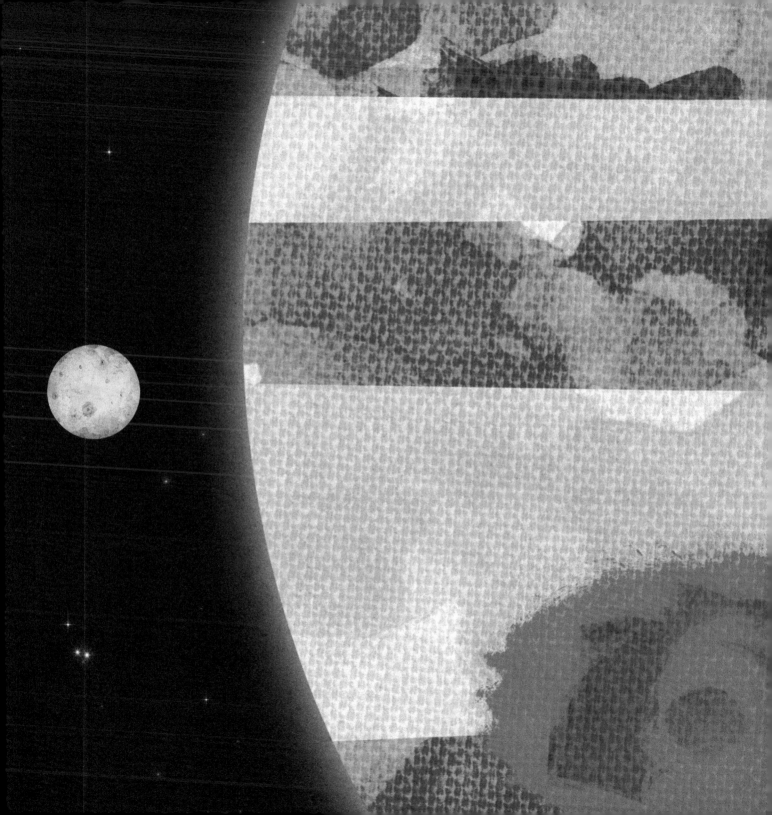

R ising plumes from Io are trailing into space.

Ice skating on Europa.
1,2,3 let's race!

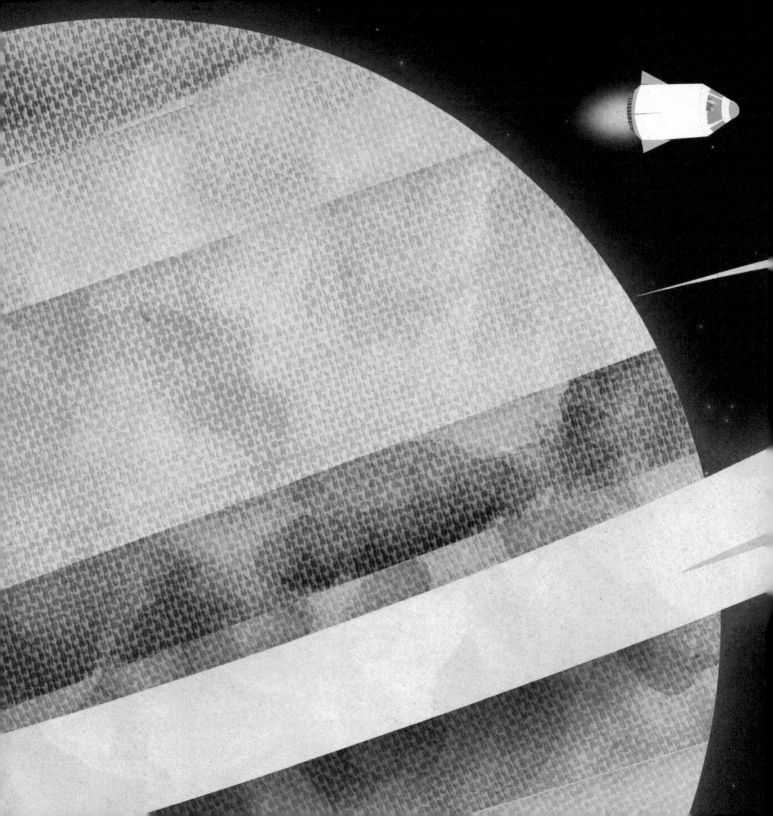

Saturn is our next stop, with more than sixty moons, and clouds of gas too buoyant to even fly balloons.

T
itan is the largest moon with liquid and thick air.

You weigh so very little, you
can fly with wings you wear.

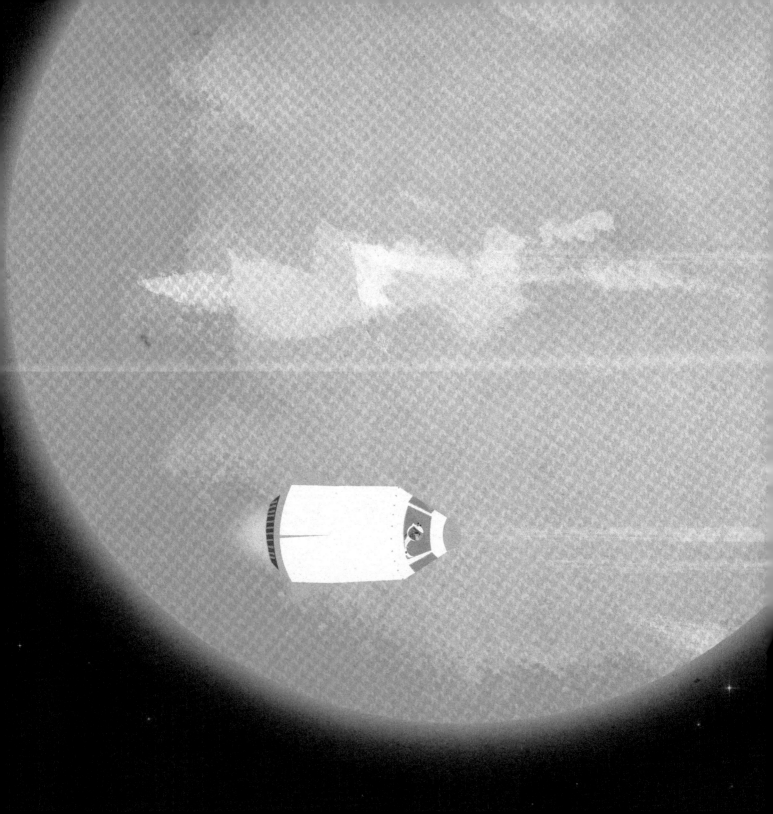

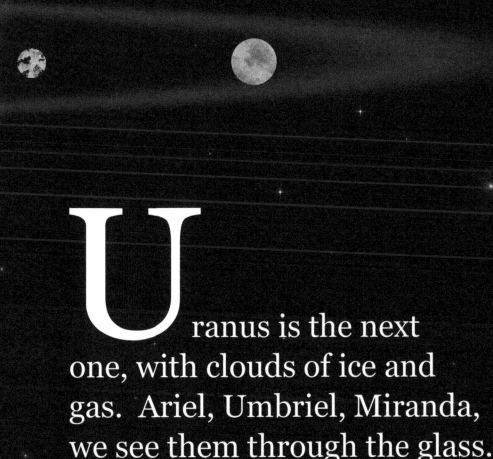

U

ranus is the next
one, with clouds of ice and
gas. Ariel, Umbriel, Miranda,
we see them through the glass.

DENSITY
2.06 G/CM3
TEMP
38 K
COMPOSITION
N CH₄ H₂O

Visiting mighty Neptune, we find a giant storm. We note that Triton's spin is different than the norm.

W

e're on to visit Pluto, the last stop on our flight. It's so far from the Sun that it's darker than the night.

X-rays racing past us, coming from the Sun. Speeding through the Oort cloud is really, really fun!

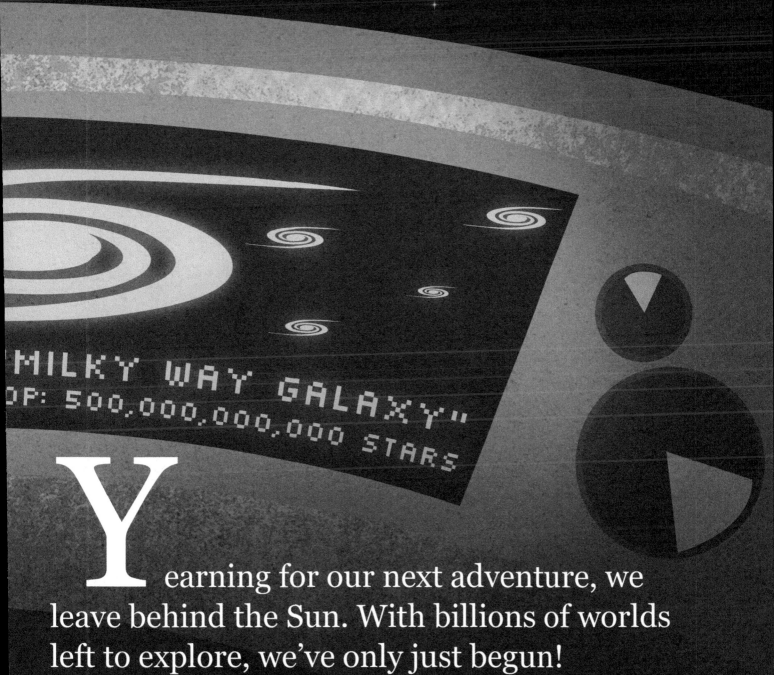

"MILKY WAY GALAXY"
OP: 500,000,000,000 STARS

Yearning for our next adventure, we leave behind the Sun. With billions of worlds left to explore, we've only just begun!

Zooming through the Milky Way, we take a glance back home. We're interstellar travelers, and through the stars we roam.

If you loved Epic Space Adventure...

"Mars Rover Rescue will get your preschooler ready
for a mission to the red planet."
-The Huffington Post

Your favorite giraffestronaut and robot are back, and
this time they're forming a rescue party to search for
a missing Mars rover. Their only hope for success is
through teamwork.

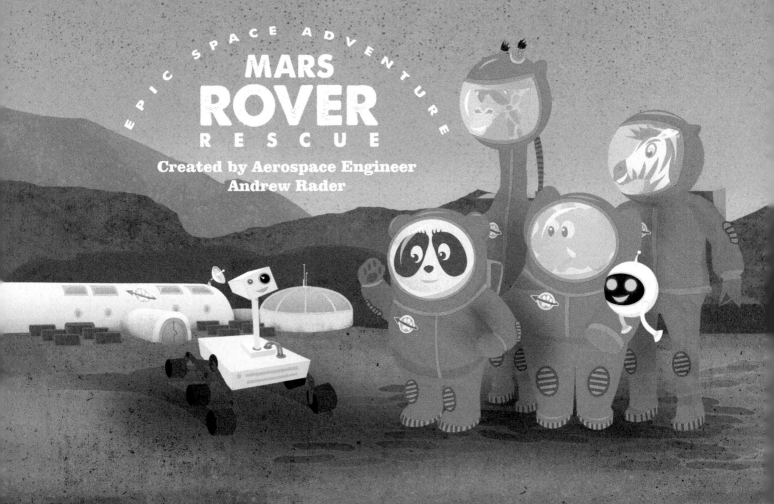

EPIC SPACE ADVENTURE

MARS
ROVER
RESCUE

Created by Aerospace Engineer
Andrew Rader

For information regarding permission, write to the publisher, StoryBook Genius, at:
4171 Crescent Dr., Ste. 101-A, St. Louis, MO 63129 or visit them on the Internet at
www.sbgpublishing.com
ISBN 978-1-941434-62-8
Text copyright© 2015 by Andrew Radar
Illustrations copyright© 2015 by Andrew Radar
All rights reserved. Published by StoryBook Genius, LLC.
Printed in the U.S.A.
First StoryBook Genius printing, May 2017.

www.sbgpublishing.com

StoryBook Genius
Publishing

Publishing
Brilliantly
Illustrated
Children's Books

CPSIA information can be obtained
at www.ICGtesting.com
Printed in the USA
LVOW06s1317100118
562540LV00030B/696/P